Contents

Safety Notice: It is dangerous to stray onto railway lines as trains travel fast and cannot stop quickly. Always use public footpaths and keep behind the fence and away from platform edges at train stations.

Bobby and his family went to London by train.

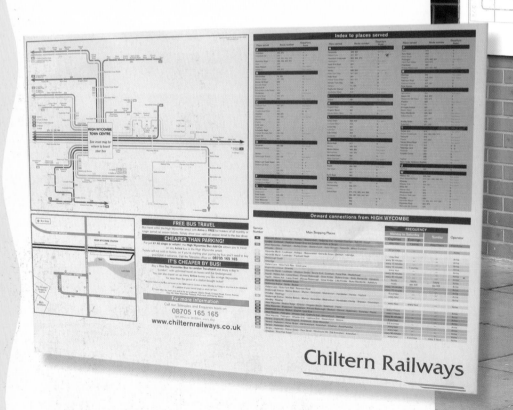

Dad bought the tickets.

The man at the gate checked the tickets.

They got on
the train.

Mum found some
seats.

Can I sit by
the window?

The train
sped by fields
and farms.

A ticket inspector clipped their tickets.

They ate their
packed lunch.

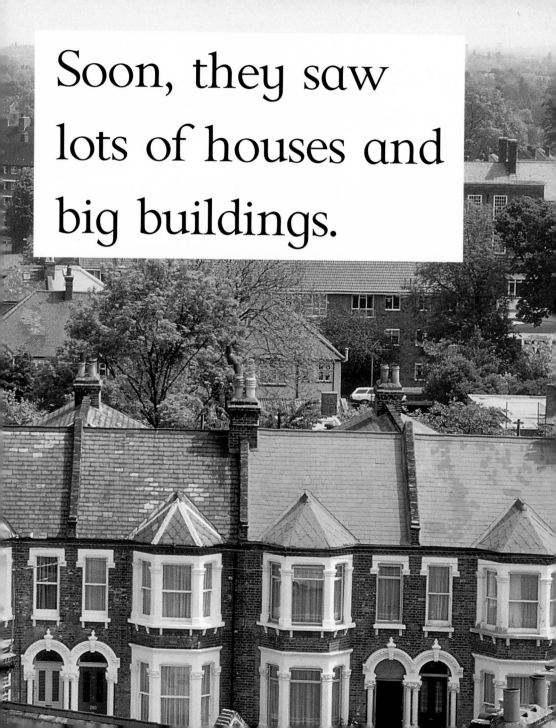

Soon, they saw lots of houses and big buildings.

The train arrived in London.

They saw the
London Eye ...

... and went to Trafalgar Square.

Time to get the train home now!

Word bank

Look back for these words and pictures.

Buildings

Farms

Fields

Gate

Inspector

Packed lunch

Tickets

Train

Window